# What TIME tuesday?

## One Man's escape from "The Beast" of Trigeminal Neuralgia (TN) through Upper Cervical Care

### Revised with larger charts and new testimonies

James Tomasi
www.whattimetuesday.com
whattimetuesday@gmail.com

International Christian Servants
www.whatimetuesday.com

# what TIME, tuesday?
(5th revised edition)

Published by:
International Christian Servants, Inc.
**www.ICServants.org**

(704) 323-9250 or (918) 606-2638

ISBN 0-9709344-4-0 978 -0-9709344-4-4

ICServants.org        WhatTimeTuesday.com
GetWellGetHealthy.com        UpperCervicalAdvoates.com

ucpatients@gmail.com        whattimetuesday@gmail.com

1st Printing — June, 2005 2nd Printing — Sept., 2005

3rd Printing — May, 2006 4th Printing — July, 2007

5th Printing — Dec., 2008 6th Printing — Dec., 2009

7th Printing — Dec., 2010 8th Printing — Dec., 2011

9th Printing — April, 2013

Cover concept and illustration: MacKensie Mathison

Printed in the United States of America

# Reviews

*Kudos! James' story is compelling, but his attitude is even more remarkable. Most facial pain sufferers simply want their lives back after recovery. Few would go to such effort to help others. God bless both of you for your efforts! You mentioned micro vascular decompression (MVD). This procedure involves moving vasculature away from the trigeminal nerve root and wrapping it with teflon or another material. We've had quite a few patients who had failed MVD (2 MVDs, in one case) and other surgeries (Rhizotomy, Gama Knife radiosurgery, etc., some multiple procedures), but have experienced excellent results with Upper Cervical Care*

**— Dr. Roger Hinson,**
**United Family Hospitals & Clinics, Beijing China**

*Congratulations on the success and wisdom of your book what TIME, tuesday? . It is heart rending and inspirational to say the least!Your concept of unselfishly providing chiropractic service to the sick and suffering is a noble and necessary undertaking and it will be achieved through God's will and blessings. May you continue to be blessed in terms of your hearts desires.*

**— Sincerely, Sid E.Williams B.S., D.C.**

*"what TIME, tuesday?" is an incredible story of an incredible journey. It parallels a walk through the Valley of Death only to come out the other side with a message that has brought hope and healing to thousands. This experience gave James a passion to get Upper Cervical Care into the hearts and minds of people around the world. If this healing could happen in James, why not you? If you have already received a healing then we encourage you to join James and Rhonda's crusade of bringing awareness to a hurting and suffering world who desperately needs caring, compassionate, dedicated doctors who are specifically trained to open "the mouth of God". Thus, more people can get well, naturally.*

**— Robert Kessinger, UC-DC**
**KCUCS Founder**

# Preface

As an Upper Cervical doctor, I listen while patients unfold their struggles with pain and suffering. I hear desperation in each descriptive plea as they describe their dismay at being dismissed and shuffled though the medical system. I am blessed to understand first-hand the quandary many patients face. These on top of the never ending cycle of pain, produce misery.

People are encouraged to believe that a pill or operation will solve their problem; that an herb can be a natural remedy, or a change in diet, exercise or fresh air will bring the long awaited healing. Others are told that a past sin is the root cause, and a new prayer will deliver them. They continually seek answers. Hope is a wonderful thing. It fuels the desire to fight and press-on in the face of adversity, but in time becomes despair when no tangible results are obtained.

I watched from afar as my parents walked this road. As children we were so delicately sheltered and protected from the pain and misery that dictated their lives. It was only later that I understood the severity of his condition. As a child it is hard to understand why your father does not talk to you; why he eats meals alone and avoids the entire family except on rare occasions.

I can recall Christmas morning, 1996, in which we spent only ten minutes with him before he retreated back to his room in order to hide the dire grimaces that belied his intense suffering. It is difficult for a child to understand the physical and mental agony that people in pain endure. Unfortunately many walls were created because of this solitude. Today I realize how deeply our entire family unit was affected by this disease, as I hear stories from other families trapped in a similar cycle of pain, disappointment and fear.

Growing up with someone who suffered created a desire to help others in similar situations. I steered toward massage therapy, appreciating the wonderful ways it helped ease pain. By manipulation of soft tissue I was able to relieve pain. My path was redirected when my dad found his recovery through a relatively unknown scientific technique.

# Preface

It was hard to believe that such a simple procedure could relieve my step-father's pain, restoring our family dynamic. However, I watched as he evolved into the happy, enthusiastic man I had once known. After seeing such dramatic change, I realized that I must learn how to change other people's life permanently, not just ease their discomfort temporarily. I did not understand at that time how Upper Cervical chiropractic worked, but I made a decision to find out.

Now, years later, I have gained understanding of the inner workings of the human body. As a practicing Upper Cervical doctor, I am able to repay the service once given to James that has benefitted our entire family. In my practice, I see the cycle of "hope and despair" in many of my patients. My reward is seeing that cycle broken, restoring faith to those in need.

I sincerely thank James for using the suffering he endured to benefit others. It was not easy to live in such pain. I am thankful that he now shares his testimony with millions who suffer, having no direction or hope.

My desire is to serve and help others, which directly stems from his journey and those who helped him regain a viable life. I pray that I may return these gifts of health to others ten thousand fold.

— **Roderick Peddy, DC**

# Acknowledgements

We extend a warm thank you to the following dear friends and family: Our special, long-time friends who share my past, my present and my future. **Steve and Sondra Grauel Cape Coral, FL** allowed me to take precious time during our visit to write this book. Steve also supports us on the mission field. He learned to make balloon-animals and attended Clown school so "Squeaky" could better entertain children on the mission field. Thanks, Steve.

To our children **Dr. Roderick and Melissa Peddy, Rion Peddy, (SC) Rebekah Peddy Smith, Mandi Tomasi, Miriam Gold, (OK) Robert and Joan Peddy (UT) and Dru and Molly Morgan, (CA)** who open their hearts and homes for our frequent visits, and so graciously share their love and our grandchildren, with our limited time.

To **Dr. Jennifer (OK)** for giving me my life back, and to all Upper Cervical doctors for their dedication to help people recover health.

We appreciate **David and Linda High (OKC)**, for their friendship and prayers; A very special thank you belongs to **Rudy and Lavonne Blanco (OK),** for supporting our endeavor in Upper Cervical for a decade. Their prayer, financial gifts and friendship were priceless in allowing us to pursue our call to Marketplace ministry.

We give special thanks for making this book even BETTER to **June and Dr. Daniel O. Clark, (NV)** as well as **Greg Buchanan, (NSW,** Australia). Their friendship, vision and passion for UC Care are invaluable to us both.

Last, we thank all the patients of Upper Cervical Care who have called or E-mailed, sharing the impact this small book had on their life. We are grateful to UC-DC's for sharing this book with thousands! We wrote it to deliver the same message of hope we heard over a decade ago. Bless you as you now share what we've experienced.

-James & Rhonda Tomasi

# TABLE OF CONTENTS

Reviews.......................................................................... III

Preface.......................................................................... IV

Acknowledgements ......................................................... VI

Table of Contents............................................................VII

Place books in ................................................................ VIII

1. God's Hidden Mystery to Perfect Health .....................1
   Charts printed with permission of Daniel O. Clark, D.C.

2. Pain: My Trial of Fire ....................................................9

3. The "Mouth of God" Speaks to My Body ...................19

4. What's the Plan? ........................................................27

5. About the Tomasis.....................................................33
   Table of dis-ease ........................................................ 44
   **SPECIFIC AILMENT TESTIMONIES :**
   Autism.................................................................37, 50
   Bed-wetting................................................................ 42
   Dizziness...................................................................... 44
   Ear Infections ............................................................. 44
   Fibromyalgia............................................................... 39
   IBS .............................................................................. 44
   Meinere's .................................................................... 45
   Migraines .............................................................48, 43
   MS .......................................................................48, 49
   TN ............................................................................... 47
   Sleeplessness ............................................................. 40

6. Testimonials from other UC Recipients.......................37
   Printed with permission of individual patients

7. Greg Buchanan's notes ............................................55
   Printed with permission of Greg Buchanan
   Upper Cervical: A Chiropractic Specialty ....................... 55

# Place books in:

1. EVERY business within a 2 block radius of the Upper Cervical office
2. Coffee houses in reading areas
3. Massage therapy clinics with therapists, and in waiting room
4. Homeopathic offices for doctor and staff members
5. Chinese herbal offices
6. Health Food store employees and owners
7. Hair salons
8. Barber shops
9. Dentists
10. Hospital waiting rooms (*One advocate put 33 books out in one hospital!)
11. B & B's in the area
12. Naturopathic doctors and staff
13. Networking groups
14. Civic organizations (Rotary, Lions, Shriners, etc)
15. Chamber of commerce (especially when you join)
16. Support group leaders of TN, Fibromyalgia, Autism, MS, Meinere's, etc)
17. Local Real estate agencies (same as with churches)
18. Local schools/universities for the teachers/instructors
19. Local churches, with a letter offering to show a movie or teach a class
20. Local small businesses
21. Local corporations (same as with churches)
22. Other local chiropractors you introduce yourself to or meet
23. Pain clinics * We've sent the movie and books to Pain clinics and received calls from patients the staff referred. THEY ONLY ACCEPT INSURANCE CASES
24. Every patient that comes through the door!
25. Local motels or hotels
26. Every business you go to each day. Someone there needs this information!

(*Leave extra's for people to give to potential patients! (Especially hair stylists!) Also, in  professional places, leave one for the dentist, Naturopath, owner, etc. but also give one to the staff members. They are the ones who will tell others many times. In clubs, offer to show the movie, "The Power of Upper Cervical" and then give everyone a book to take home. Better yet, ask a patient to do this for you!)

# 1

# Gods' Hidden Mystery
# For Perfect Health

I'd like to introduce you to one of the best kept secrets in the world; a secret so powerful that it can extend your life by years. It affords you a pain-free, symptom-less lifestyle without drug dependency; much closer to divine health. It allows you to enjoy a long, full life instead of spending each waking moment in a pain-racked or disease laden body.

This secret involves a simple, relatively unknown scientific procedure that maintains head/neck alignment, thus allowing the brain to communicate with each part of the body without nerve interference. This science is otherwise known as UPPER CERVICAL HEALTH CARE.

The head is designed to rest perfectly balanced on top of the spine. This is quite a feat since the human skull weighs between 8 and 14 pounds. This would be similar to balancing a bowling ball on the end of a broomstick.

The critical area necessary to regain and maintain health is at the point where the head and neck join. Housed within this area is the brain's communication pathway, the brainstem, where health and healing messages are relayed to all parts of the body. When your head is on straight, correctly balanced atop your spine, your innate life force is free to communicate through this amazing doorway.

# HEAD/NECK MISALIGNMENT
## (BODY IMBALANCED)

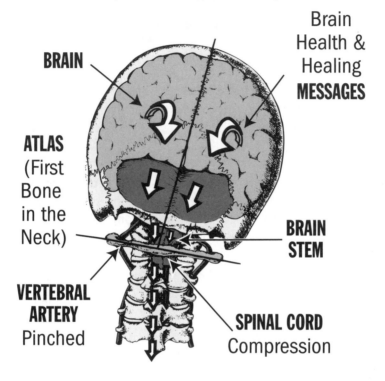

**BRAIN**

Brain Health & Healing **MESSAGES**

**ATLAS** (First Bone in the Neck)

**BRAIN STEM**

**VERTEBRAL ARTERY** Pinched

**SPINAL CORD** Compression

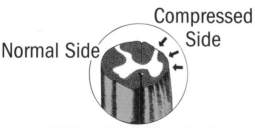

Normal Side

Compressed Side

**SPINAL CORD CROSS SECTION**

When the head is in perfect alignment on top of the neck, the brain is free to send these messages down the spinal cord, out over the nervous system to all parts of the body.

When our head and neck is not in perfect alignment, the brain is restricted from sending healing messages to some parts of the body. Each part of the body that cannot communicate effectively with the brain will begin to develop health problems.

The brainstem is the delicate headquarters for all body functions and acts as a connector and communicator for all healing. When this area is opened correctly, allowing the brain to receive/send proper signals, we grow health and remain healthy. If the head and neck gets out of proper position, the brain will not get the necessary signals and hear the body's desperate cry for help.

Passing through the center of this critical area where the head and neck join, are over 7 trillion nerves. They send and receive messages that monitor and maintain all body functions.

Some of you may relate to my previous health issues. I thought I was born with an allergy to horses, cats and freshly mowed grass. My eyes watered and swelled shut when I encountered these irritants. Each breath constricted as spores or dust agitated my breathing follicles. I gasped as the allergens reacted on my malfunctioning immune system.

It was also normal for me to side-clip my ingrown toe nails in order to divert their painful growth. I thought it was normal for my eyeglass frames to be uneven and cockeyed. They didn't fit right. One ear piece was always higher than the other when I laid my eyeglasses down on a table. I thought I'd been born with crooked ears, bad toes, allergies and asthma.

Take a look at yourself or someone you know. Is one ear higher than the other? The next time you're in front of a mirror, look at your eye brows; is one lower than the other? How about your shoulders? Are they the same height? Does your head sit in front of your shoulders? Do you have a small hump on your back?

# HOW IS SPINAL CORD COMPRESSION AND BODY IMBALANCE DETERMINED?

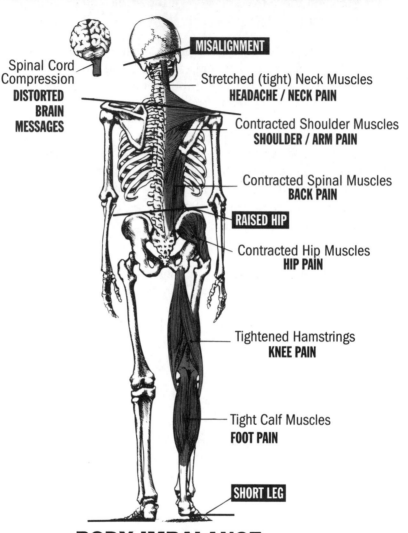

Spinal Cord Compression
**DISTORTED BRAIN MESSAGES**

MISALIGNMENT

Stretched (tight) Neck Muscles
**HEADACHE / NECK PAIN**

Contracted Shoulder Muscles
**SHOULDER / ARM PAIN**

Contracted Spinal Muscles
**BACK PAIN**

RAISED HIP

Contracted Hip Muscles
**HIP PAIN**

Tightened Hamstrings
**KNEE PAIN**

Tight Calf Muscles
**FOOT PAIN**

SHORT LEG

## BODY IMBALANCE

All of these symptoms were relevant to me. I accepted all of these irregularities as just being natural. Simply put, I accepted as normal what I had become aware of in my body as being different or uncomfortable, just like I accepted my height and the color of my eyes. I was totally unaware that one area in my body governed all these ailments, signifying to those who understood the scientific principle of this area, that I was simply out of balance.

My wife and I cringe every time we watch 'America's Funniest Home Video's'. With each fall, accident or 'whack' to the head, we know that the person involved just misaligned the top two bones and will develop symptoms of deteriorating health in the years to come. I visited an Upper Cervical doctor several years ago who related a story about a family visiting his clinic. They asked him, "Are you one of those doctors that work on the bones called, the 'mouth of God?'

The question took Dr. York completely by surprise. "This is not a normal inquiry," he mused. "Well, Sir," he responded, *"What is the mouth of God?"*

The father shared a fascinating tale about taking his family to India. They sought a cure to their various ailments. They went to have the mouth of God manipulated by Fakkirs, an East Indian mountain sect.

After listening for an hour about their incredible journey, he concluded that it indeed was the same area of the body. He recognized the area as the upper cervical. They were amazed and delighted as he explained that the area he realigned was exactly what they had flown to India to have manipulated.

The doctor realigned the mouth of God for each of them. They maintained the crucial check-ups necessary to ensure their alignment stayed balanced until their bodies healed enough to hold the correction, and they never had to travel overseas for care again.

This story illustrates the power of Upper Cervical corrections. This is the most critical area of our body since it affects the instructions sent to every organ and cell. If we want to regain and maintain good health, the brain must be able to communicate with all parts of the body without interference.

Let's consider a foundational teaching. Do you agree that God intended for Adam and Eve to live indefinitely in the Garden of Eden? It was just the two of them. Right? Or was it Adam and Eve and Dr. Steve with the pharmacy on the hill?

The reason Dr. Steve and the pharmacy wasn't included was because God made provision for health from a source other than drugs or organ removal. He could, and can, do anything; but His design intends us to live in perfect health. He said we were created in His image. He also designed our bodies to heal themselves by His Innate life force flowing from the brainstem to the brain, through the upper cervical area, to every cell of our body.

This vital head/neck area can be misaligned during a fall, an accident, or sometimes during the birth process. Forceps used as an aid in giving birth can cause undetermined misalignment to this delicate area, as can extended head rotation. A premature twist or elongated pull of the head, just like an accident, can cause head/neck misalignment to occur resulting in symptoms which persistently deteriorate until health gives way to symptoms labeled as disease.

When head/neck misalignment occurs, if it is not corrected, it will restrict the communication from the brain to the body, creating health problems. These problems continue to grow worse until and unless, the communication is restored. The Upper Cervical correction is specifically designed to correct head/neck misalignment which then restores body balance, reactivates brain communication and allows the body's natural self-healing process to begin.

Visualize yourself watering with a hose. Can you imagine how the pressure decreases when the hose is kinked? There is a reduction of water pressure equivalent to the amount of pressure linked to the kink. The decreased pressure affects the ability of the hose to work effectively. Aha!! The same thing happens to our bodies. If we have a kink in our hose [the upper cervical area], we will not receive100% of the messages sent to vital areas. We cannot expect to stay well when this process is interrupted.

But, I'm getting way ahead of myself. Let me start at the beginning and share how my wife and I discovered the mouth of God and the specialists of Upper Cervical Care.

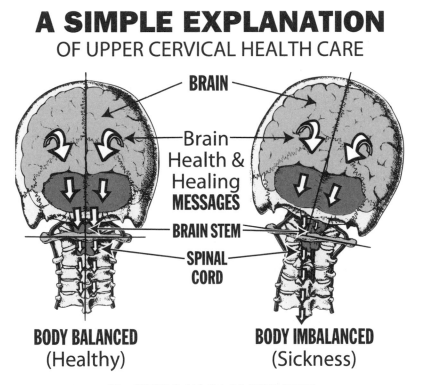

# A SIMPLE EXPLANATION
## OF UPPER CERVICAL HEALTH CARE

BRAIN

Brain Health & Healing MESSAGES

BRAIN STEM

SPINAL CORD

**BODY BALANCED**
(Healthy)

**BODY IMBALANCED**
(Sickness)

what TIME, tuesday?

# 2

# Pain: My Trial of Fire

I first met the beast, as I now refer to my previous pain, in the summer of 1986. I started over in business and felt comfortable enough to take care of minor health concerns. One such necessity was over due dental work, so I made an appointment with a local dentist.

It was supposed to be a routine root canal. I reclined in the chair; eyes closed, drifting off into la-la land. I remember the Novocaine injections, my mouth becoming cottony numb, and the dentist working on my right jaw for several hours. He mentioned a nerve wrapped around the tooth root presented problems, then sent me home with a prescription for pain killers.

By late afternoon, the numbness wore off, and the right side of my face experienced stabbing spikes of pain. It was as though the pain instinctively knew where to jab for the greatest effect of heightened distress. I panicked; this pain was unlike anything I had experienced. The spikes came and left, but each spasm was worse than the one before. Although I had a high pain tolerance level, this pain stretched my coping mechanism past that threshold.

I called the dental office and they suggested I fill my prescription, then return the next morning. I did. The bottle read, "Take 1 pill every 4 hours as needed." I immediately took four pills and went to my bedroom hoping to escape the electric jolts through sleep. An agonizing ache remained in my jaw area below the right eye. Utterly exhausted, I somehow dozed off around midnight.

In prayer, I asked for this nightmarish pain to end, but it was still raging as I arrived at his office early the next morning. The receptionist assured me that I'd be fine. As soon as the shot of Novocaine was injected, the pain went away leaving me with sweet relief. My dentist explained that I might have a dry socket. He cleaned and repacked the area.

The numbing effect of the Novocaine allowed me to return to my business during the afternoon. The numbness kept me from chewing or talking well, but I didn't mind; I was just thankful that I no longer felt that throbbing, horrific pain.

By early evening, the Novocaine wore off. The pain returned with strong, continual electric jolts to the right side of my face centered in the jawbone. My face hurt worse than I remembered the day before.

Welcome to my new life; one saturated with overwhelming pain. I had no idea at that time, but I stood on the brink of a gloomy hole of despair, trapped for the next twelve years. I had no way of knowing it would entail a hopeless journey exploring mazes with no guarantee of escape. It was my first experience of living in a deep, black tunnel of unbelievable misery and hopelessness.

I struggled with the loneliness of facing this unmanageable beast that refused to provide any long-term relief. There was no external sign indicating where the pain was, so no one understood the agony I faced each moment. I slowly retreated from my church, family and business contacts.

Then remarkably, I awoke one day, and the pain wasn't there. I thought it was a random incident. Little did I know that the nature of this beast was to leave for long periods of time, only to return with greater intensity and to last longer with each episode.

In 1990, following a new attack, my bride Rhonda searched for a remedy. She took me to MD's who prescribed pain medications. One medical doctor mockingly asked, "Has his PHANTOM pain returned again?" It was obvious he thought I was seeking drugs. After being told by several that the pain was in my head, or I was a drug addict, she looked elsewhere for answers.

She found an oral surgeon who lanced my upper and lower gums, scraping them for any viral infection, before stitching them back up. The only good thing about that trip was the Novocaine shot that brought relief for four hours of the painful two week recovery.

When that failed to relieve the pain, we were directed to a neurosurgeon. He identified the beast, giving it a name, and us a diagnosis. Trigeminal Neuralgia, or TN as it is better known, is described as an incurable nerve disease. There were no known pharmaceuticals which worked on nerve pain, so he prescribed drugs approved for muscle spasms. He warned us that they could cause liver cancer. He explained that this condition was more common in women, but there was no known cause or cure for it in either gender.

He prescribed Neurotin, a drug used to help control seizures in Epileptics. He warned that it would take a few weeks to build up in my system. By the first month's end, I still felt every spasm, had a constant dry mouth and got dizzy every time I tried to walk. He added Dilantin, which affected my equilibrium so I could no longer drive a vehicle. I suffered with additional side-affects, but received no relief from the pain. Each day was spent praying the endless cycle of pain would diminish. My wife determined to find a way out of this parody. We visited churches where they advertised healing evangelists. We tried chiropractors, Manuka Mushroom Tea, and various herbal remedies. All of these ended with the same result: no escape from the spasms wreaking havoc on our lives.

A normal day became one episode after another of pain spiking up into my face from my lower jaw, straight into my cheek bone. Let me give you a brief description of what it was like. Have you ever had an exposed nerve in a tooth? Hurts, right? Consider taking a piece of ice and touching that nerve. The result is intense, right? Well, this felt like I had an exposed nerve in every tooth in the right side of my mouth AND a mouth full of ice. It felt like the ice touched all the nerves simultaneously as the pain escalated past excruciating. It rendered me incapable of swallowing or spitting out the perceived ice to stop the pain; instead, each piece stayed locked onto every tooth nerve causing fire to shoot through different muscles of my face.

When the pain was there, I cried, whimpered and became reclusive, avoiding everyone, except my wife. She was my faithful caregiver, as well as the recipient of the brunt harshness of my ill-tempered desperation.

If asked a question, the piercing spikes electrified my face as I spoke. Though I desired to brush my teeth, the pain was so bad, that I became unable to coax myself to put the brush in my hand, much less into my mouth. When I tried to eat, the movement of food touching my lips irritated the pain, causing the spikes to increase in strength and duration.

Without warning, the nerve pain stopped. I convinced myself I had outlasted the disease. Or, I'd been healed by the visiting evangelist we'd seen a few days before. My life returned to normal because the pain left, but fear that it would return was always just underneath the surface.

Nerve pain doesn't reflect injury like bruised or damaged tissue. It hurts, but there are no tell-tale signs that let someone sympathize with you. Since it is intangible, only those who learn to read the pained expression in masked eyes knew I was being tormented.

When the pain stopped, I looked exactly like I had one moment before, except I could laugh, talk and be myself again. Other than my wife, most people never realized that just moments before I was on the verge of screaming due to the electrifying pain. No one related when I described the pain. They looked at me as if to say, "Everything looks normal."

Have you had a similar experience? Perhaps there are people who think you're crazy when you describe that unseen pain that keeps you from participating in ordinary activities. If so, don't think you're alone; there are many victims of unnoticeable pain.

Every three to eight months the pain stopped. Every moment was filled with dread, wondering when the pain would return. I remember walking down our driveway to the mail box one morning. A slight breeze brushed my face and a spike of pain announced its return. "I'm back!" the pain taunted me. I felt the tell-tale tingling tinge on my lips assuring me my brief reprisal was nothing more than a bad joke. I was thrown back into the throes of captivity.

Another time, as I slipped a shirt over my head the pain spiked as the material brushed my jaw. Spasms engulfed me as the spikes of pain jolted through my face. "Here we go again; the beast is back in control," I thought to myself. With each reprieve, I hoped I had 'gotten over' it. I learned to cherish every moment the pain was not master of my life.

Do you have pain so bad it ruins your life? Has someone told you that the pain you feel is in your head; suggesting that you're making it up? If so, I understand.

My mind focused on the pain during every waking hour. "How can I stop it? Why is it here again? Why is this happening to me?" All the while I thought how I, as a man, should be able to handle this. "But this torture is more than I can stand," was the over-whelming response of my mind.

I told myself, "Deal with this for today." I didn't want to, but it kept my sanity. Does this sound familiar to you? By 1995 I was on three prescriptions. At times my wife tripled those dosages in response to my cries. I took regular blood tests to indicate liver cancer.

My neurologist added new trial drugs recommended for TN patients. By 1995 I was taking three prescriptions. At times my wife gave into my pleas for help and tripled those dosages. Every 6 to 8 weeks they did blood tests so the laboratory knew if my liver still handled the damaging effects of the drugs.

Not only did I hurt incessantly, but I dealt with all the side affects. I would be so disoriented, that at times I could not find the door to the bathroom in our master bedroom. I would hit my head on the door jam, bruising and scraping the skin off. My mouth stayed so dry, that my tongue felt like sand paper. The sad thing was that I was still fully aware of the pain, just unable to focus on anything around me. When it was there, the pain prevented me from concentrating on anything else.

Our bedroom became my inner sanctuary where I hid during the dire episodes. I kept the bedroom dark. Subtle desperation became a way of life. I originally tried to attend church, operate our business, and maintain a cell group in our home on a weekly basis. But gradually, I eliminated everything as I tried to cope with this beast.

Rhonda encouraged me to go to church for a while, but the people brushed my face when they hugged me, which sent stronger spasms of pain escalating through my jaw. Others offered to pray for me, while some asked me what sin I'd committed to get myself in this mess. In self-defense I decided to hide in our home. My life became an isolated nightmare in my personal hell.

Some mornings I awoke to the sensation of a powerful electric drill delivering electrical jolts into the back of my eyeball. Without warning, the drill would reverse and feel as if it were pushing my eyeball out of the socket. It was so unbearable that I would scream out loud with the pillow clutched tightly over my face.

Other times the electric currents would move to the tip of my tongue. Then it felt as if electrodes hooked on the tip projected 220 volt electric currents into it. My tongue curled inward as I clamped down on it with my teeth in an attempt to divert the pain.

When it was in my eye or on my tongue, Rhonda called Dr. Li at

TCM Health Clinic. She'd found him during a search of local pain clinics. She'd been discouraged because the minimum charge for pain assessment was $1500. A receptionist took pity on her once she learned we had no insurance, revealing he'd just left their clinic to open a private practice. He assured her that he could develop a Chinese herbal brew that would wean me from the drugs, accomplishing the same minimal relief without the side affects. She slowly switched me to the awful tasting tea, which probably saved my liver. Meanwhile, anytime the pain was in my eye or tongue she called him.

Dr. Li was a Chinese medical doctor who used acupuncture to move the pain, but who could not stop it. He took me to a quiet room as soon as I arrived and used acupuncture needles to move the spikes to a location that was more tolerable. Sometimes I was able to sleep for an hour on his table following several sleepless nights. We were both grateful for this treatment and his sympathetic concern, but disappointed that we'd reached another dead-end.

We found no explanation for the beast coming or going. I desperately anticipated a time when 'it' would leave forever. Not one thing I did governed its departure; the pain left and over-took me at will. However, we did notice that strong emotions or stress caused the spikes to intensify or even bring on a new attack.

For years, Rhonda researched TN. One operation coated the nerve, another cut the nerve, resulting in dysfunctional facial muscles. The cost? A mere $40,000, which we didn't have unless we added a second mortgage to our home.

She joined chat lines where patients shared their personal experience with drugs, homeopathic remedies and operations they'd tried. Rhonda noted the probability of success. None were very encouraging, and all the operations were costly. Some patients reported going blind, having the pain switch to the other side or receiving no relief at all. Others lost all use of their facial muscles. Overall, most were discouraged following touted operations which failed to deliver the much sought after relief.

Victims of this debilitating disease spend hours on chat lines describing their lonely, defunct lives. They expose poignant details of suffering combined with the frustration of failing to beat this unconquerable condition. Everyone searches for the answer that will provide an escape hatch into lasting deliverance, allowing them to survive this anomaly of nature.

TN is known as the suicide disease. We completely understand why people choose this way out. I planned how I would end my life for months. I confided to Rhonda that I could no longer bear the pain. She pleaded with me to hang on. Without her, I truly believe I would have ended my life years earlier. It was her steadfast encouragement that there was an answer somewhere that gave me that thin thread of hope I clung to. Finally though, I decided I couldn't bear the agony any longer. I placed a small pistol in the night stand on my side of the bed. Unbeknownst to her I chose the day I would end my life. I could no longer endure the endless days of suffering having no relief in sight.

I lost hope after twelve years of living with the beast as my taskmaster. The last two years, except for a brief three month reprieve, the pain never stopped. I decided that suicide was my only way of escape.

I wasn't insane. I was just too tired to fight anymore. It took weeks of reflective planning to make the decision to kill myself. I chose 5 pm the following Tuesday in February, 1997 to end it all because she took our son Rion to soccer practice at that hour and would be out of the house.

That was Thursday. I prayed she would get compassion from those who might misunderstand and blame her. There is a stigma that rests on the family of someone who ends their life. I hated for her to bear that, but I was more absorbed in my desperation, than I was concerned about her acceptance in the community. I didn't know then that a spirit of suicide was controlling my thoughts, making me feel like I was in control. I believed this was the only way to stop the pain, and I believed God had called me 'home'.

The next evening Rhonda came upstairs. "I'm going out for groceries, honey. Don't do anything stupid while I'm gone," she told me sternly, looking deeply into my eyes.

She knew I was desperate because I'd told her so many times, "I can't stand it any longer." Neither of us knew that her decision to leave me alone that night would change both our lives forever.

# Poem for all who are in pain...
## in the fire of UC trauma
## IN THE FIRE

Oh, that I would remain strong,

and, my hope would never tire,

as again I find myself,

standing in a lake of fire.

Oh, that in the heat of it I will not burn,

and, my faith in my Protector would grow higher.

Although the flames burn all around me,

to come out of them, and glorify Him is my desire.

This trial by fire to some looks like humiliation,

my past already laden in muck and mire.

But, God's truth, and His esteem are upon me,

and, I know Satan's accusations make him a liar.

To keep my eyes fixed, and my faith unwavering,

is all God my Sustainer requires.

When I walk away untouched by these flames,

Let it be God's faithfulness that others admire,

and, not me, and my own strength, for it is not of myself,

that I have the ability to not be consumed by this fire.

**-Trisha Curtiss**

# 3

# The "Mouth of God" Speaks to my Body

Rhonda left our home during a gusty Oklahoma windstorm. With tree branches waving their long arms above the car, she drove toward a grocery store. Suddenly, a lady on the Oasis Christian radio station out of Tulsa asked, "Do you have pain you just can't bear? Have you been told, You'll just have to learn to live with it?" Her questions exhibited compassion and concern, which grabbed Rhonda's attention. She rarely listened to that channel, so she wondered why the dial was reset. Turning up the volume, she drove slower, listening intently.

The woman related her personal experience of dealing with pain for eighteen months. She passionately shared the knowledge of a relatively unknown scientific technique that relieved her suffering, delivering her from her prison of pain. Rhonda patiently sat in the car listening to the program. She refused to go into the store until they announced how to get more information. The woman mentioned that due to the complexity of the technique, there was less than a thousand of these doctors in the world. Rhonda was uncertain what or who these doctors were, but she knew she had to find the closest one.

When she returned home, she requested information about the broadcast. She then bounded upstairs saying God had sent a way of escape from this abyss. She related what she'd heard, but I didn't believe her; my hope was gone, and I'd made the decision to escape this chasm of pain my way.

The next morning Rhonda received a call from an Upper Cervcal doctor, seventeen miles north of us. "Can you help Trigeminal patients?" Rhonda questioned.

"I know of cases where TN patients responded well to this procedure. I can't guarantee anything, but I believe it will help," was the response. Rhonda had a deep conviction that this was our answer, so she scheduled an appointment.

Quickly she rushed up the stairs to our bedroom with her announcement, "We're going to a different kind of chiropractor's office."

"Another chiropractor?" I whispered with clenched teeth. I had tried several chiropractors without results. Utter dismay flashed across her cute little face.

"She does that Upper Cervical technique I heard about last night." Since I really wanted to please my wife these last few days, I decided not to contest her over the issue.

"We can't go on Monday since she just moved into her office, but," she excitedly exclaimed, "she can see you on Tuesday!"

I merely nodded, quietly thinking how I hated to leave my precious wife. Instead, I tolerantly inquired, "What TIME, Tuesday?"

"Ten a.m.," she answered, smiling like a child who just received permission to do something important.

I nodded, silently thinking, "I can do 10 o'clock to make her happy. Yeah, I can do this one last thing for her. "Assuming my usual position on the bed, I leaned over the headboard on my knees. While facing the wall I bit into a pillow, trying not to moan too loud. Time crawled while I waited through unbearable suffering for Tuesday to arrive. We left our home early. When we finally arrived, the pain had intensified from all the jostling in and out of traffic. Amazing how we take the simple things of life for granted; like driving a car, talking, eating or brushing our teeth.

Dr. Jennifer instinctively understood that any movements made while she took X-rays aggravated the pain. After completing them, she sympathetically suggested that we wait. She wanted to correct me before I returned home. That was a divine decision on her part. She didn't know that I would never have returned had she sent me home with just an appointment for another day.

After a forty-five minute analysis, she asked, "Do you remember your Mother telling you after you'd been in some sort of mischief, 'You better get your head on straight'?"

I nodded my head in response. "Well, perhaps she knew more than you thought she did. This is just what I'm about to do," she finished, looking at me with those compassionate, blue Norwegian eyes. "I'm going to put your head back on straight so your body can heal itself."

She explained that she needed those X-rays to see if my head should be corrected. She verified that my head was leaning forward and tilted several degrees.

She had me lie down on my side on a low table as her tall frame towered above me like a giant angel. I felt her hands apply a gentle pressure just behind my ear. I felt no different, but remember her saying confidently, "Let's take another film to see where your head is now."

I sat in a chair in the dark X-ray room while she processed the films. Silently I thought to myself that this was all a waste of time and money. The pain was as intense as ever, and I wanted to retreat back to the safety of our bedroom. I made a note of the time on her wall clock, counting the hours left.

The films on the view box indicated that my head was on straighter. She scheduled an appointment for me on Thursday. "You might need another correction then," she told me.

I thought to myself, "Sure!" When we got inside the car, I looked at Rhonda and said, "What a rip off. I felt nothing move, and the pain is just as bad as it was before I got to her office."

"Remember, James, the woman on the radio said, "It took years to debilitate, and it may take some time for healing to begin." She glanced at me encouragingly, "Please just be patient and give this a chance. You may not get immediate results like she did, but I believe this is what we've been looking for and that it will work."

I was disappointed, which made me more determined than ever to complete the suicide. "Why didn't you just give her the money and let me stay home today?" I responded sharply. I knew my defeated life was over; I had nothing left to hope for. Our last attempt had just proven fruitless. "Just take me home," I mumbled with disgust.

Once we arrived home, I went upstairs to our bedroom. I settled back on the pillows, fixing my eyes on the clock. If only it was 5 o'clock, I would be out of this perpetual cycle of misery. "It'll be over soon," I told myself. "Pain can affect my life for another few hours, but then I will take control and end this." I drifted in and out of consciousness for an hour or so. When I was fully awake, I realized that the pain had stopped!

"Rhonda," I said excitedly, seeing her across the room. "I can talk! The pain isn't there." Within 10 seconds of that hopeful statement, the pain was bearing down as intensely as it had before.

She knew from the look in my eyes that it was there again. "That was a break in your cycle," she encouraged me. Don't give up...this is going to work."

I looked at the clock on the night stand. "Yes, something's going to work," I thought to myself. "That single bullet will absolutely work for sure."

Within the hour, it happened again. I had a brief interruption of the pain. This time, the relief lasted between 20-25 seconds. I was afraid to believe that this might be my answer. But, for the first time in what seemed like an eternity, the pain had stopped in midcycle. The interruptions of relief were distinct and absolute, outside the standard regression. Normally, when a cycle of pain stopped, the spasms would reduce in length and strength over a period of time. These spasms would just stop, and then restart with the same intensity.

I began to weep, desperately wanting to believe that this might really be the answer we'd prayed for. I decided to believe that the Lord had given power to this angel named Dr. Jennifer, and, just maybe, she had broken its power over me. I made a decision to let the clock roll past 5 o'clock, and see if the pain would continue to decrease. I still didn't have any real hope, but these brief relapses had given me a glance into what life could possibly be without pain.

By the time we returned to Dr. Jennifer on Thursday, the intensity level had reduced 50%, from a level ten to between a four and five. The spikes were lasting about 20-30 seconds, and coming only a few times each hour. Within 11 days, after three corrections, I had no pain.

Becoming pain free gave my life back. I moved freely around the house, talked to the family, and went anywhere I pleased. I was thankful Rhonda had put me on the tea a year prior. There was no withdrawals because she had weaned me off the drugs when I started drinking the tea. I eventually became confidant enough to lay the tea aside also.

I was skeptical, but slowly accepted that we were free of the beast. I had no idea how that little movement Dr. Jennifer made worked, but I couldn't argue with the results.

I hadn't attended church in over ten months. People were amazed that I was there again. We excitedly shared the little we knew about this 100+ year old science that had given me my life back. Our pastor, and many of my church family who had known me during this painful time, suffered with various ailments. They too scheduled appointments with Dr. Jennifer. We suggested to anyone we spoke to that this might be their answer. We simply believed it could help anyone with any problem.

We were thrilled with all the testimonies we heard from people we referred. The waiting room always had someone we'd talked to sitting there when I'd go for a routine maintenance check. It was almost like an alternative church service. We constantly told anyone with an ailment that they should try Upper Cervical for their malady.

My friend Steve suffered with low back pain for years. We explained that the Upper Cervical doctor would put his head back on straight, and that would help his lower back. His reaction was like most of us, "There is no way those top two bones affect the pain in my lower back."

Steve's major concern was for his wife Sondra; she suffered for years with migraine headaches. We insisted this doctor would get rid of them. "Sondra's headaches are in her head, not her neck," he challenged. "I really don't know how it works, I only know the pain I had all those years is gone," I said.

"Ok, we'll go." Several years later, Steve said his lower back pain stopped after his second correction and Sondra hadn't suffered with a severe migraine since starting her maintenance care.

We shared my story with anyone who would listen. Many were surprised strangers who we pulled aside, sharing our story of being healed through Upper Cervical Care. During the first year, we sent over 300 hurting people to Dr. Jennifer.

Then, after 13 months without pain, the short, intense spikes signaling a new series, started again. It was back!

Doubts flooded my mind. I wondered if the pain had receded on its own, and now was back to take me into a deeper hell. Could the doctor really stop this pain again, or had it just been a fluke?

Following another set of X-rays and additional corrections, the pain stopped again. I made a decision. I decided to stay on a maintenance program to ensure my head stayed balanced as long as necessary.

I've always changed my automobile's oil every 3,000 miles. If my tires get out of alignment, I have them re-aligned. I decided to invest the same diligence with my body that I show for my vehicles.

The office receptionist told us one day they made a game of tracing each patient back to James. I heard later that they traced over 1500 patients to us.

We knew this technique worked, but had no scientific understanding of how or why it worked. We were not concerned about our lack of understanding. We just wanted other people to know where to find an answer for their hopeless situation. We didn't know then that we had ventured into a calling from God that would require learning even more about these bones we affectionately call *the mouth of God.*

# 4

# What's The Plan?

About a year after my healing, Rhonda wrote a letter to the woman she'd heard on the radio. She wrote about me, and included stories of our friends who also got well under Upper Cervical Care.

Our biggest frustration was sharing my story with people in other states, who weren't willing to drive 12 hours for care under our doctor. The lady on the radio responded to her letter, sharing how to locate other Upper Cervical doctors.

We traveled for her organization for 18 months, 2000-01, meeting other UC doctors. This evolved into a God-given birthing of His vision for branding Upper Cervical. Our travels led us into following God and birthing His vision of branding Upper Cervical. *Levites in the Marketplace*, not yet published, details the conviction to stop being business-people and instead follow His leading to bring public awareness about these UC DC's.

It is the sequel to *Whose Deal is It?* that expounds on my battle with Trigeminal Neuralgia in greater detail. This books' theme is to make believers aware of the process when people leave their past lifestyle and begin to utilize new values, build character and leave old ways and friends. It emphasizes the transformation process involved in pleasing a higher power with our choices, instead of one's-self. *Whose Deal is It?* is the sequel to *Feed the Tiger*, my testimony of being transformed from a self-centered entrepreneur who used people to make money, into a born again believer who met Jesus Christ during imprisonment. The three books meld into our love for Upper Cervical Care.

You're probably thinking, "Wow! How nice of James and Rhonda to reach people desperately searching for an answer to their hopeless situation. I wish I could help someone like that, but I can't explain Upper Cervical like they do."

If you want to help in this quest of restoring health, there is a plan. No, not a multi-level marketing plan, but a plan none the less; one of awareness-based giving. You enter the fringes of the plan as you read this book. If you haven't already, you must make a decision to experience the benefits of Upper Cervical Care. As you experience optimum health, you enroll in the plan. The plan involves each of us sharing the message of this healing science with individuals who need it. Details about advanced membership can be found at www.UpperCervicalAdvocates.com.

Dr. Jennifer never asked for anything above her customary fee. Her entire focus was on how to help me. I knew God used her to save my life. She was unaware of this, but none the less, she saved me from death. I was so grateful, that I could not just walk away and forget what she did for me.

I asked myself, "How can I best help Dr. Jennifer?" I desperately wanted to make sure she stayed in business. I didn't hurt any longer, but if the pain returned, I wanted her around so she could put my head back on straight.

I figured she might struggle financially, since what she did really helped people get well. I reasoned that when patients get well, they no longer need her service and probably revert back to normal living, giving no thought toward ensuring that she needs replacement patients. That meant she might go out of business, or move, which was a major concern to me. Now, years later, we've learned that many Upper Cervical doctors DO go out of business because their patients get well.

I knew she was single (at the time). I had a couple of single sons, so I wondered if an arranged marriage was a possibility. No, I decided, that probably won't work since one is 13 and the other is still in college. I next considered buying property close to her home, but it was too far from our client base. The thought that she might have to move was disgruntling, since she was my lifeline.

My business sense told me that her office was not crowded, which meant she didn't have a lot of patients. If I really wanted to help her, or to make sure she stayed in business, I should fill the waiting room. That would do it, just keep her busy. That was my assurance she was always there in case the 'beast' returned.

Over the next few years we constantly referred people with health problems to her office. Then, during prayer in 1999, we received a commissioning to take Upper Cervical doctors on mission trips. Some of the doctors had been on mission trips before, and were excited about doing it again. They wanted to help those less fortunate.

We made our first mission trip in July, 2000 to Costa Rica with 36 doctors and ten servants. Over 22,000 patients were touched with this healing grace. The testimonies of healing and spiritual avocation are recorded in our book *Levites in the Marketplace*.

I have never encountered a group of doctors more passionate about what they do. It never ceases to amaze me how dedicated these Upper Cervical specialists are in their desire to help others. Most have personal testimonies of changing career directions because of the healing they either witnessed or received through this science. Many share with us their personal testimony of how they were called into their particular technique within this science. I discovered that each Upper Cervical doctor has more passion about this science, and exhibits more dedication to their philosophy, than members of most religious organizations I've met.

We are specifically designed by God to enjoy good health. It is unnatural to accept an ailment as normal. The adage, "Oh well, that's just how it is as we get older," should not be acceptable. It is not the truth. God created us to be healthy. When we know the truth, the truth will set us free. And the truth is, once we keep the head and neck in alignment so the brain can accurately communicate with all parts of the body, our body will heal itself. All symptoms we experience, whether painful or just annoying, relay the message that the upper cervical has a misalignment. The testimonies at the end of this book verify the results.

Once health is restored, we encourage you to partner with the non-profit organization International Upper Cervical Patient Advocates Association (IUCPAA). As a member you receive materials and training that make it easier to share information about this science and its benefits with both strangers and family members.

## NOTE FROM RHONDA ON "THE PLAN"
I encourage you to become part of The Plan by joining Upper Cervical Advocates (IUCPAA). Together, we can take the message of health and healing to the world.

Upper Cervical Advocates is a grass roots movement that empowers patients to speak and witness about the science of Upper Cervical Care. The goal is to raise awareness of UC Care through public speaking venues, knowledgeable hand-outs, and volunteer opportunities. Donations are accepted to provide funding for those less fortunate, assistance for students dedicated to becoming Upper Cervical doctors, and provide housing for those traveling great distances that need extended Upper Cervical Care.

Marketing materials, books, pamphlets, DVD's and cards that assist in explaining the Upper Cervical science to friends, family, and strangers are available on the web site. "How-to" videos and Newsletters provide education and direction. There are always positions open for volunteers on local, regional and national levels.

To join, ask a UC doctor for an application form or download one from  www.UpperCervicalAdvocates.com.

— **Sincerely, Rhonda Tomasi**

# 5

# About the Tomasis

James Tomasi was a talent scout and entertainment promoter in the 1950's, a Venture capitalist (Hong Kong, Thailand and Vietnam-1960's), Entrepreneur (Europe, Fiji-1970's), commodity broker for White Star Shipping and Ramasi, Inc. (1970-80's), vice-president of sales for Safetel, Inc. and president of Telephone Audit Service (1990's). After being ordained in 2000 he served as a deacon before becoming an associate-pastor. James is the current president of International Christian Servants, Inc., a world-renowned speaker, author (*Feed the Tiger* and *what TIME, tuesday?*) and Marketplace chaplain. He received an honorary Doctorate of Chiropractic from Sherman College in December, 2007 and shares the "Chiropractic Advocates of the Year Award for 2007" with his wife Rhonda. He is a spiritual advisor for Upper Cervical Health Centers and speaks at public venues on behalf of Upper Cervical. He utilizes his insight as a former businessman to bring vision and direction to UC- DC's by assisting and providing guidance under the auspice of an Upper Cervical advocate.

Rhonda Tomasi holds a B.A. in Business Management/Marketing, was an ICEA certified Childbirth instructor for 12 years,

CFO of Telephone Audit Service, and CEO of Electric Jazz. After being ordained in 2000, she served as a deaconess. She served as the mission coordinator for ICS and UC HIM. She is coauthor with her husband James of *Whose Deal is It?*.

Rhonda and Greg Buchanan founded the Upper Cervical Advocates Association (IUCPAA).

James and Rhonda speak at civic organizations, on radio and TV and patient meetings. In universities they encourage doctors and students to become masters of their unique science.

They believe UC Care is the answer for many Christians who have searched for answers just like they did.

Their vision is to see Upper Cervical Care utilized in rehab centers, prisons, pain clinics and asylums. They want the science validated through proper research proving that people with depression, as well as other mental and physical disorders can be helped when UC care is provided. They desire to educate people on the original vision of D.D. and son, B.J. Palmer, the discoverer and father of chiropractic.

They want people to understand the BIG IDEA of Innate health. Their dream is to host television and radio programs where they interview people whose lives have been impacted through Upper Cervical Care. They see themselves as a voice crying in the wilderness, "FIND HEALING AND HEALTH THERE!"

Contact the Tomasi's by emailing them at
whattimetuesday@gmail.com

To better understand upper cervical science or to locate an Upper Cervical doctor world-wide, please visit UpSpine.com Or GetWellGetHealthy.com.

## OUR Goals Are To:

1. Build Upper Cervical advocates worldwide
2. Empower patients to share their story
3. Supply patients with materials, training and strategy to promote the Upper Cervical practice in their local community
4. Establish a voice of 100,000 plus Upper Cervical patients who will lobby for the recognition that Upper Cervical care rightly deserves
5. Establish scholarship funds for needy patients and long-term housing care for patients who travel long distances
6. Educate small business and Corporations on how UC Care can decrease employee sick leave and expensive insurance premiums

## The Plan

Please USE this book to put The Plan into action:

1. Schedule an appointment to see if your head is on straight.
2. Tell someone they may find hope through Upper Cervical Health Care

REMEMBER: YOU DID NOT CATCH A DISEASE or get PAINFUL SYMPTOMS overnight. It will take TIME for your body to totally balance.

**James Tomasi, Spiritual counselor and Business advisor**
**Rhonda Tomasi, Health Coach and Business consultant**
**Upper Cervical Advocates in Marketplace ministry**

**whattimetuesday.com**          **UpperCervicalAdvocates.com**
**GetWellGetHealthy.com**       **ICServants.org**

## EMPOWER IUCPAA

Build a voice of wellness in YOUR community! Join by downloading a membership application from UpperCervicalAdvocates.

We've heard anecdotal evidence supporting the disappearance of symptoms listed below from an atlas correction. Maybe you KNOW someone with one of these you should share this book with?

| | |
|---|---|
| ADD/AHD | Irritable Bowel Syndrome |
| ADHD | Learning disorders |
| Allergy relief | Loss of sleep |
| Arm or Shoulder pain | Meniere Disease |
| Arthritis | Menopause symptoms |
| Asthma | Menstrual problems |
| Autism | Migraine headaches |
| Bed wetting | Multiple Sclerosis |
| Bell's Palsy | Neuralgia's |
| Breathing difficulties | Neuritis |
| Carpal Tunnel | Numbness |
| Cerebral Palsy | Parkinson's Disease |
| Chronic pain or infections | PMS problems |
| Colic | Reduced tumor size |
| Constipation | Restless leg syndrome |
| Depression | Ringing in the ear |
| Dizziness, Vertigo | Sciatica or back pain |
| Ear infections | Scleraderma |
| Epileptic seizures | Scoliosis |
| Eye & Ear infections | Seizure disorders |
| Fibromyalgia | Sinus infection reduction |
| Flu symptoms | Sore throat |
| Hacking cough | Swollen knees |
| Herniated disc | T.M.J. Syndrome |
| High blood pressure | Tendonitis |
| Hyperactivity | Tingling sensations |
| Immune System deficiency | Trigeminal Neuralgia |
| Infertility | Whiplash |

# 6

# Testimonials from other UC Recipients

## Autism, ADHD, ADD and Therapists

My story begins in July 2005 when I took my three year old son, Dillon, for his annual checkup. As I filled out his developmental questionnaire my heart sank; my fears were confirmed that my little boy was not progressing at an age appropriate level. He was slightly behind on his gross motor skills, however everything else was quite delayed. His speech and fine motor skills were at the bottom of the chart.

Dillon's pediatrician recommended the school system evaluation for him. Dillon was labeled developmentally delayed based on their assessments. He also suffered from attention deficit hyperactivity disorder. He was placed in a classroom setting with speech and occupational therapy in October of 2005.

When his school year ended in June of 2006, we saw only minor improvements in his development. He was practically uncontrollable. I had read many articles and books on autism and planned to talk to this Pediatrician at his four year checkup in July about having him evaluated since he showed far too many signs to ignore any longer. I also planned on asking about ADHD medication. I knew the side effects of these medications were quite profound, but I was exhausted what discipline tactic I hadn't tried, yet nothing worked.

I told my mother about my decision. Her response changed our lives forever, "I attended a seminar where Dr. Paul spoke on the benefits of Upper Cervical Chiropractic. He talked about the side affects of Ritalin and other drugs."

"If Dr. Paul doesn't want kids on these drugs," I retorted half joking, but still hoping, "he needs to do something about it." She handed me his card for a free evaluation. I thought it was a long shot, but I was ready to try anything. I prayed, then scheduled an appointment.

After the first adjustment, Dillon slept soundly all night for the first time in his life. He smiled at me when I spoke. Each adjustment brought more milestones. After two weeks, he came to me and gave me hugs and kisses. Within a month, he was a brilliant little comedian and a joy to be around. He was an energetic, healthy, happy four year old boy. His only obstacle proved to be just one little bone that needed to be co rectly placed back into the proper position.

At Dillon's four year checkup, one month after beginning treatments, I again filled out the developmental charts, but this time with a smile. Dillon was at or about average in every category. His gross motor skills and critical thinking skills were at the top of the charts. When his school started back in August, his teachers were stunned. Dillon now meets all his goals in record time, and they make new ones to keep him challenged. He starts kindergarten in the fall, and I have no doubt he will do wonderfully. His life will never be the same, thanks to God and to Upper Cervical Care with Dr. Paul.

**— Robin, Charlotte, NC**

# Fibromyalgia Testimony

I had suffered an ongoing chronic pain for 23 years. Pain in my back and legs became an agony which froze my entire body as it grew worse each year. I had exhausted every type of doctor and test you could imagine, being finally diagnosed with "Severe Chronic Fibromyalgia". I was advised to take disability and make the best of my life. I was so heavily medicated my life became totally dysfunctional. The pain was relentless and the drugs were killing me. That is when I decided it was better to die than live. I was in a dark, black place.

Then a true GOD thing happened. I was watching TV late one night; the show was about Upper Cervical Chiropractic. The lady on the show had the same symptoms as I and she had found help. My husband yelled from downstairs, "Hey Hon, you watching this?" The next day we made an appointment with the Upper Cervical doctor on the show.

He was different, from the first meeting he restored my hope. I did not get relief right away. He assured me I would, encouraging me not to give up. I didn't; what other choice did I have anyway? Slowly and surely I felt freedom; I got my life back. With each appointment the pain begin to melt away. I gave up the prescription drugs one by one and soon they were all out of my body! My mind cleared and I began to live my life with full gusto! Today, I don't miss my maintenance check-ups. I stay drug free and drink plenty of water. I stead of being bound to the bed with agony and self-defeating thoughts, I look forward to each day with a heart full of gratitude. I now manage a fitness gym where I spread the news about Upper Cervical Care to those without hope. Thank you God, and Thank you, Dr. Ray! My life has been saved!

— **Linda, Charlotte, NC**

# Headaches...Back pain...Sleeplessness... Depression... Hair loss...Inability to sit/stand... Severe NervePain...Chronic pain over body... Reduced temperature in legs

I slipped at work on salad dressing, injuring my right knee. The simple accident became a long, painful nightmare. I did physical therapy, rest and various medications, but my pain increased. A new doctor scoped my knee, which preceded another operation and a final diagnosis of Reflex Sympathetic Dystrophy.

The next four years found me in two pain clinics, taking spinal injections for the pain, and 11 different drugs. Next was the dorsal spinal stimulator, then a medical detox. I saw 13 specialists before I was diagnosed with Fibromyalgia. I tried herbs, acupuncture, chiropractors, meditation, yoga, and was headed for a morphine pump.

At that point, all hope lost, I heard about Dr. Tom. Following the first correction my change was unbelievable: I felt taller, the nerve pain in my legs was gone, headaches left as well as the pain in my knee. I was sore, but felt like a new person.

Over the past year the hair on my leg has grown back, the hypersensitivity in my knee is gone, my nails are back to normal without ridges or holes. I have muscle tone, sleep and feel great and can do anything I want.

You, your amazing instrument and God have given me my life back.

— **Carol, Kansas City**

## Ear Infections and Antibiotics

I had never really given any thought to the healing powerof chiropractic, before our third son Matthew was born. It had helped me when I injured my back at work, and so I respected chiropractic care for back pain. I never dreamed that a specific chiropractic technique would play such a crucial role in the healing of our young son.

Matthew seemed healthy. But at 10 days, I noticed a "rattle" in his nose. After persisting for a few days, it was diagnosed as "congestion" by his pediatrician. It then became a sinus infection, for which he was prescribed an antibiotic. That led to a year and a half of constantly going to doctor visits because of bad ear infections.

Matthew wasn't in day care, or around cigarette smoke, and he was breast fed, the things that were supposed to prevent respiratory and ear problems. I was very frustrated with the constant sickness. The pediatrician had no answers except to continue with the antibiotics. Eventually Matthew was on breathing treatments around the clock (every 2-4 hours), which led to surgery having tubes put in his ears.

During another round of testing the pediatrician discovered Matthew's white blood cell count was exceptionally high, while his red blood cell count was low. He wanted to monitor this so we began periodical blood tests. By this time Matthew had been on 19 rounds of antibiotics, and after sitting up night after night in the recliner with Matthew (so he could breathe easier), my back and neck began to really bother me.

I decided to seek chiropractic care for my back and neck. While at the specific Upper Cervical clinic, I began to read the literature. I was surprised to read that Upper Cervical Care could help with Matthew's problems. I talked with Dr. Rob and he said to bring Matthew in, that he could help. By this time the pediatrician watching Matthew's blood cell counts, had decided to send him to a hematologist if the count didn't reach more normal levels by our next visit.

Matthew received his first upper cervical adjustment at the age of 14 months. Within hours Matthew's nose started to drain. I cried. It was the first time in his life, his nose had drained without medicine! The following Tuesday Matthew's blood was tested again. The pediatrician called me personally to give me the results. He said, "It's a miracle! I can't explain why, but Matthew's blood cell counts are at normal levels, so there's no need for further testing." I knew why those levels had dropped.

I knew that what Dr. Rob had done made the difference. Within a few months of beginning Upper Cervical Chiropractic care, Matthew was completely off all breathing treatments, and has never had another antibiotic.

Matthew is 5 years old now, and is not bothered by the sinus or ear problems that plagued the first year and a half of his life. This is due to the Upper Cervical Care he receives at the clinic.

— **Laura (Matthew's Mom), Missouri**

# Bed-wetting

Our 15 year old son was so embarrassed about his nightly incontinence that he would cry and beg to skip school. He retreated from everyone. Following his first Upper Cervical correction, the incontinence diminished, and over a few weeks disappeared completely!!

—**An Anonymous mother, Kentucky**

# Ice Fall Brings on Debilitating Headaches, Sneezing Episodes & Intense Shoulder Pain

As I slipped on the ice in 1999, my arm went behind my back, resulting in both neck and shoulder pain. I received cortisone shots for the pain, initially, but decided to 'just endure' it for several years. Over time I developed sinus headaches, allergies and excessive sneezing.

I heard about Dr. Bruce, and decided to try him. The first day after my first adjustment, I felt different. Several weeks into it, I realized that I HAD NOT BEEN SNEEZING!! There were such changes in my body, that I asked to work for Dr. Bruce and Tonya. I am thrilled to be in an office of healing like this.

—**Terri, a "patient" employee, Kentucky**

## Migraines and Neck Curve

Prior to finding Upper Cervical Care, I suffered from a number of physical ailments. My main problem was migraine headaches five to six times a week. Not only were my migraines constant, I was having ringing in my ears, cold feet and hands and my right leg appeared to be shorter than the left. Even the simplest of tasks were difficult.

After just one adjustment by Dr. Smith, my symptoms disappeared! I used to joke that I should own stock in a popular pain reliever. I was told by a conventional chiropractor that I did not have a curve in my neck and would need 2-3 years of traction therapy to correct my curve.

I was under the care of this chiropractor for about one month with no improvement but was experiencing more pain. I knew right then that the traction therapy was not for me and I stopped treatment all together. I found Dr. Smith by referral and I was shocked to find out that so many of my problems were associated with my atlas being out of alignment.

— **Krystl, Huntington Beach, CA**

# Pastor Abraham reports from Ghana after Doctors from God make second visit

Hello: The Lord's name forever be praised! You have performed a Godly assignment in Ghana and you are blessed. The phones are rolling in and the people wonder when again? My answers have always been, "We are working on it, and pray that God's will be done." The excitement is great and expectations are high.

A man suffering from stroke for the past ten years unable to lift his arms and legs has now been able to lift and move the limbs after his adjustment; the family is rejoicing!

The question is, "WHAT NEXT?" The feeling is if enough time and at-tention is given to every individual, a lot of diseases will be healed.

I can't agree more with Dr. Rob in his email to me, "I haven't heard of anything that is insurmountable."

I bring you love and greetings from Ghana.

**—Abraham &Tina Asare, family and the Ghana Team**

# Ear ache, Irritable Bowel, Nausea and Hypo-thyroidism Disappears!

I had ear-aches several times each week. I suffered with allergies, a runny nose and sore throat constantly. My stomach gave me problems, including bloating, irritable bowel, gaseous symptoms and nausea. I also had pain in both shoulders and my back. I was tired and had low energy. My final diagnosis after a colonoscopy, was Hypo-thyroidism.

A friend told me about Upper Cervical Specific Care, so I tried it. Six months later, I am off Allegra, my stomach problems are basically gone, and my sore throat and ear-aches are completely gone! I rarely have shoulder pain, and my energy level is much better!! Probably the most miraculous of all, is that my thyroid is actually getting better! My medication has been cut in half, and my doctor says I may get off it all soon. God has truly used Dr. Bruce and Upper Cervical to heal me.

**— Georganne, Kentucky**

# Relief Found for Dizziness and Eye Problems for 75 year old Woman in KY

I was 75 in 2003. I had trouble walking. I was forced to use a walker and a cane. I was dizzy and had eye problems. It was difficult to think. I decided to try Upper Cervical Care. I am no longer dizzy, have given up the cane, and best of all, my thinking has improved. Thank you, Dr. Bruce.

**— Rubye L., Kentucky**

# Meniere's Disease: Dr. Kevin and his mother's Testimony

Our youngest son, Kevin, complained of nausea and the liberating episode of nausea, dizziness and projectile vomiting. This marked the beginning of the most tumultuous period in our lives. Our faith was soon put to a test that none of us could have imagined.

Our pediatrician diagnosed Kevin with Meniere's disease, but sent us to Dr. Compton, an ENT specialist. He mentioned several things that could be wrong with Kevin, including a fistula, tumor, or leukemia! No parent wants to hear any of those words! We spent an entire year testing for the proper diagnosis. However, in the meantime, Kevin was so sick that he fell on the floor with the dizziness, experienced hearing loss, and spent a large portion of his time throwing up over the commode. I begged Dr. Compton to send me to the best doctor they could find.

We traveled to a 'world renowned specialist' for Meniere's disease. Our hopes of finding a solution let alone a cure was quickly dashed as he told us that the only alternative was to destroy Kevin's balance nerve. According to this specialist, Kevin would have to go to the Lahey Clinic in Boston for this treatment. After receiving this treatment Kevin could never run, play soccer, go swimming in a pond or lake again, and worst of all, never go to bed without a light on in his room because this treatment would destroy his body's 'computer mechanism'. The three of us went home with heavy hearts because we believed there was no cure!!!

We traveled to another very well known medical facility. However, this time we chose a surgery performed by a knowledgeable ear specialist. A shunt was placed in Kevin's ear to reduce the amount of fluid that builds up during Meniere's disease. We so hoped this would give Kevin the much needed relief from debilitating nausea and vomiting. At this point, the hearing loss was dramatically reduced, while all the symptoms remained.

The disappointments continued, while hospital visits increased. The only two people that I had confidence in were Dr. Compton and his audiologist. Theses two were always there when we needed them. Unfortunately though, they could only tell us "there is no cure, and Meniere's can stay for years, completely destroying the hearing; it also could leave as quickly as it had come!"

By this time, Kevin was missing some 90+ days in school. We asked strong prayer warriors in two states to pray that Kevin receive healing or a medical miracle.

Our miracle came when Dr. Ray, an Upper Cervical Doctor, called me "out of the blue" asking to speak at the Meniere's support group I'd formed. I told him that I did not know if I believed in chiropractic care but that I had an open mind and scheduled him to speak.

(Kevin's Mom & Dad) (Kevin) My life changed the day my mother received a phone call from a doctor in NC. He said that his specific procedure could help Meniere's victims. How could a chiropractor help if a doctor from Duke, Vanderbilt, and Boston could not? Although there was doubt, we went to see him.

That day I had been sick in the morning, and I could not hear. This doctor went through the synopsis of his procedure, and told me that he knew what my problem was. He understood and had been successful in relieving these symptoms in others. I received my first Upper Cervical Chiropractic adjustment that day. In a fifteen minute period I regained my hearing. That alone was enough to secure me as a patient for life.

Although the symptoms of the disease did not go away immediately, this doctor gave me my life back so that I could function as others did. He gave me the ability to return to school, to be part of a state championship soccer team, go to college where I have met my most trusted and life long friends and in hindsight gave me the ability to help hundreds of thousands of suffering people. I am a recent graduate of chiropractic school and opening my own Upper Cervical clinic, under the guidance of the doc tor that saved me.

I owe him my life, and everything I cherish, including my wonderful wife and children. How amazing that a simple procedure can reconnect the innate intelligence that God put inside us, with the body that longs for control and efficient operation! There were times during my youth I questioned God. How could a loving God isolate and strike his own children? But the more educated I become about the body and its own innate healing capability, the more it solidifies my relationship and trust in God.

The God that created us and the intelligence that operates in us knows that obstacles in the path causes us to cherish and endure our means of salvation. I have found my path and I do cherish it. And for that reason, I thank the Upper Cervical doctor and his hands God used to heal me, each day. I leave you with this quote:

*We never know how far reaching some thing we may think, say or do may affect the lives of millions tomorrow.*

— **B.J. Palmer**

## TN Pain Free In Ohio

I visited my doctor last week for my maintenance treatment. He gave me a copy of your book! I was so excited that you wrote and distributed it along with the Testimonials from other UC recipients of Upper Cervical Chiropractic around the world. My Upper Cervical doctor was very excited for me to read your book because I was the first TN patient that he had treated, and I became 100% pain free after only 2 treatments! I have been 99.9% pain free ever since. And with regular treatments I remain that way.

I am so happy that you have had the same success. Thanks again for the book. I am getting ready to mail it to a friend with fibromyalgia and chronic fatigue syndrome, in hopes that she will seek help.

Please do not hesitate to contact me if there is ever anything I can do to help you in this cause!

— **Sherri, Ohio**

# CHRONIC Head, Neck & Shoulder Pain

An automobile accident resulted in a four year search for relief of chronic pain in my head, neck, shoulders and back. I spent over $40,000 in consultations with multiple specialists, including neuro-surgery and orthopedic specialists from the University of Maryland and John Hopkins University. While considering the lack of results my sister obtained from surgery for similar pain, I continued my search.

At a Christmas party, John told me about the work of an Upper Cervical doctor in Atlanta. His explanations made such sense, that I scheduled with you the day after Christmas. Your X-rays and analysis revealed the same problem, but your answer involved a noninvasive, painless technique that worked like a miracle. No pain!

Each time I experienced a relapse over the last 9 years, you used your Upper Cervical knowledge and I quickly responded. I now explain to people with similar experiences and a background of trauma or accidents how profoundly this science can change their life, and bring long lasting results of a pain-free life. There are some who refuse to believe something so simple could help them; but those who accept Upper Cervical Care in place of traditional treatment plans are grateful and tell others just like I do.

The good news is spreading. We are happy to be part of the UC family and are forever indebted to you for your brilliance and diligence in perfecting the Upper Cervical technique you use to change so many lives. God bless you, Dr. Roy, and your wonderful family!

**— Judith & Dana, Salisbury, Maryland**

## Pain: Top of head, base of head & neck

I was diagnosed with multiple sclerosis and told I would never walk again. After an unapproved treatment from Germany, I was able to use a cane and walk. On my second outing, I fell backwards on a sloping sidewalk, hitting my head. As I awoke after a brief black out, intense pain engulfed my head and neck. After fifteen years of complaints about the intense pain in my neck, base of my head and top of my head, I gave up any hope of finding relief.

For a year the monthly injections by my neurologist offered brief reprisals from the suffering. Dr. Ramon finally suggested I try an Upper Cervical doctor who would work on my head/neck area. I met with you the next week. That thing you do with your instrument performed a miracle! As we rode home after my visit I kept saying, "I can't believe it! No pain!"

You had told me that it might take several visits to get me "in perfect adjustment", but instead, after only one adjustment by you, Dr. Roy, I am pain free! Bless you for caring so much to perfect and develop an instrument to correct the Upper Cervical area so others can be pain free. I pray many patients will find you and become free of pain like I have. Thank you from the bottom of my heart.

— **Belle, Atlanta, GA**

# Two Autistic Sons...
# One Upper Cervical doctor

Following the diagnosis of Autism in both my sons in 2000, we sought Chiropractic as a source of help. Our chiropractor guided us regarding nutrition, cleansing agents and provided spinal manipulations. After limited success, he suggested we try an Upper Cervical doctor. I was quite skeptical of the idea that adjusting one vertebra could make any difference. I didn't believe the atlas could be out of alignment since I didn't recall a fall, accident or intense birth trauma for either of them.

Chad was delayed in communication skills, while Max was affected in both communication and motor skills. Both boys showed improvement right away. The day after Chad's adjustment, his teacher told me his comments were very clear, and in longer utterances. I noticed eye contact and speech improvement. Max also responded with noticeable improvement right away. He rode his bicycle through the grass for the first time.

When either regressed, I took it as a sign for another correction, after which, their improvement continued. Max required more corrections, but both boys have a calmer demeanor, and great improvements. Max has been promoted to a higher level class.

Recently a nationally recognized leader in Autistic children evaluated both boys. Her opinion is that neither fits within the autistic spectrum any longer. Although they are still deficient in some areas, I recognize chiropractic and especially Upper Cervical, as an integral factor in the dramatic successes of change. I will continue their care as long as there are issues of concern. I am sincerely appreciative of the opportunity Dr. Roy's work provided my sons to escape the world of autism.

— **Ray, Atlanta, GA**

# UC Illustrations

One UC doctor shares this example in his health talk. A young girl falls off a bike when she's six. She gets up, looks ok, and continues her normal activities. BUT, her C1 rotated out of its normal position. As a result, the brainstem signals to her body are reduced and certain nerve signals are impaired

By fourteen she has cramps with heavy menstrual periods. She takes pills to relieve the symptoms. By seventeen, she has a small lump in one breast so small that it is undetectable by her physician. By twenty-seven, she looks healthy but she suffers from fatigue, and is tested again. The lump is now detectable, and has grown for fourteen years. She undergoes surgery, radiation and chemotherapy to deter further cancerous growths.

IF SHE had received Upper Cervical Care following the bike accident, she would never have grown the lump, or suffered with female problems.

Philip Atkinson, in "A theory of Civilization", states *projected figures show that a total of 164 million people, approximately 56 percent of the US population (over the last 10 years) have been treated unnecessarily by the medical industry...*He identifies an estimated 999,936 deaths induced by inadvertent medical error in his link below. This equates to SIX JUMBO JETS crashing everyday for a year. The Nutrition Institute of America quotes MD's and Ph.D.'s who report that more people die each year from Iatrogenic disease (medical professional-related mishaps) than from heart disease or diabetes. To learn more, view these sources for expanded details on Iatrogenic disease: **www.iatrogenic.org, www.ourcivilisation.com/medicine/usamed/deaths.htm,** as well as **www.yourmedicaldetective.com/public/335.cfm.**

Think about it: Don't you want to bring security of health to your family members and avoid the possibility of becoming a statistic in an AMA journal? You can...choose health. Schedule an Upper Cervical check-up today.

— **Sincerely, Rhonda Tomasi**

## NOTE FROM RHONDA ON RESOURCES

Greg Buchanan, an Australian Upper Cervical advocate (UpCSpine.com) and Dr. Daniel and June Clark, (UpperCervicalIllustrations.com) offer informative sites and materials for the promotion of Upper Cervical. Our hope is that their ideas help you achieve Total Wellness. We all agree that holistic sciences are helpful following the atlas correction. Some options MAY BE necessary by certified professionals before complete wellness is obtained.

Many Upper Cervical doctors focus on ailments like TN, Migraines, MS, autism and Meniere's. UpcSpine.com offers research papers on how symptoms respond under Upper Cervical Care. Consider supporting a patient scholarship program in a local clinic.

Other resources available include Dr. Kerry Johnson's book, I'm Sick and Tired of Being Sick and Tired. He details Six Keys to Health, with UC being the foundation for physical, nutritional, spiritual and emotional health.

Judith Bowman shares the story of her daughters' diagnosis of cancer in 'The Fiery Furnace of Cancer'. She and Ted provide valuable insight to those facing cancer and list resources and laws regarding rights in the medical system for both patient and parent.

Several other books, videos and movies have been produced, including 'The Power of Upper Cervical' ,'Upper Cervical Care' and Health Talk I, II and III.


Order books, CD's, movies and DVD's at

whattimetuesday.com or GetWellGetHealthy.com

General Chiropractic has good points and benefits many people; however, Upper Cervical Chiropractors are specialists who receive advanced training to do specific, specialized corrections on the c1 and c2. Only those trained to take specific views of the atlas/axis and are skilled in correcting the subluxation should be allowed to touch your neck.

**An authentic Upper Cervical specialist will do the following:**

1. X-ray the Upper Cervical area in a specific way
2. Analyze films of the C1C2 in a specific way
3. Correct the C1 or C2 in a gentle, specific manner
4. Will NOT roll your neck to the left or right and guess
5. Will NOT adjust you every time you go in

## KEY Points to REMEMBER:

1. Technique results will be influenced by the skill, training and experience of the doctor
2. You MUST give your body time to heal itself. Long-term problems take longer to heal than recent trauma
3. Provide your body with adequate rest, water and nutrition during the healing process (Read about water PH benefits on GetWellGetHealthy.com)
4. Avoid stress as much as possible. Stress moves the atlas out of alignment
5. BE PATIENT. Healing takes time, and comes via Innate directives
6. If satisfactory responses do not happen within a reasonable time-frame, ask for a second opinion or new X-rays. Consider consulting a holistic professional from GetWellGetHealthy.com for assistance with incidental issues.

Become an Upper Cervical Advocate. YOU ALONE May BRING THE MESSAGE OF HOPE Someone Longs To Hear.

We all agree that patient education and knowledge will win the war over illness and disease. We trust the preceding chart and information enhance your journey to wellness and health.

Check for Holistic practitioners at GetWellGetHealthy.com

# 7

# Greg Buchanan's notes

Over years of research, I have developed what I believe to be necessary steps, for a person who is ill, has a chronic condition or has tried everything, but has failed to get better. The following steps will improve their state of health. This approach requires coordination with a number of professionals, as well as an understanding of the changes the body undergoes over time through the healing process. Since there are many avenues to health, please understand that these are OUR opinions, based on OUR experience and research.

Additional research, an explanation of the major Upper Cervical techniques and a World-wide list of UC DC's is available at UpCSpine.com

— **Greg Buchanan, Australian Upper Cervical Care advocate**

## Upper Cervical Chiropractic

There are many procedures taught in Chiropractic schools, but THIS SPECIFIC technique of Upper Cervical, (alignment of the c1or c2) was determined in the research findings of Dr. B. J. Palmer (developer of Upper Cervical Chiropractic) in the 1950's as the solution for 73% of all causes of disease. His findings were based on the documented treatment and response of over 23,000 patients. We experienced for ourselves, along with many others, that Upper Cervical usually corrects the problem, resulting in complete relief.

Recently papers were published showing that correcting the atlas resulted in symptoms of Parkinson's, Meinere's, TN and MS disappearing.

Occasionally someone needs a tune-up in other areas, as Greg's chart indicates. We encourage you to complete your health plan by visiting GetWellGetHealthy.com after you 'get your head on straight'. Sometimes it takes proper nutrition, dental work, massage therapy or meridian balance to complete the goal of optimal health. There are lists of holistic professionals that may benefit you in your quest for total health on the website. Take time to review the articles, nutritional testing and holistic, green health products available there.

Remember: Make a list of friends and family members who came to mind while you read this book. Get a copy to them. Stories of ailments are categorized by page number in the front Index page. Mark the page for them with a note.

Finally, you received this book from someone who cares about you. Please give it to someone YOU care about.